MEMORY

STICK

A scrapbook
of thoughts, happenings,
hurrahs, ideas and
conversations I
have had

POLLY SMART

summersdale

MEMORY STICK

Huck & Pucker is an imprint of Summersdale Publishers Ltd

With research by Anna Martin and Stephen Brownlee

Images © Shutterstock

Huck & Pucker
Huck Towers
46 West Street
Chichester
West Sussex
PO19 1RP
UK

www.huckandpucker.com

Printed and bound in the Czech Republic

ISBN: 978-1-909865-08-2

Substantial discounts on bulk quantities of Huck & Pucker products are available to corporations, professional associations and other organisations. For details contact Nicky Douglas by telephone: +44 (0) 1243 756902, fax: +44 (0) 1243 786300 or email: huck@huckandpucker.com.

THIS BOOK BELONGS TO

....

WHAT IS MEMORY STICK?

IT'S A PLACE TO STICK
YOUR MEMORIES, OF COURSE!
A PLACE WHERE 'THE BEST
IDEA EVER' JOSTLES FOR
ATTENTION WITH YOUR MOST
EMBARRASSING MOMENTS;
WHERE TICKET STUBS AND
AUTUMN LEAVES ARE STASHED
FOR SAFEKEEPING, BECAUSE
THEY REPRESENT SO MUCH
MORE THAN THE SUM OF
THEIR PARTS - EACH ITEM
REPRESENTS A MEMORY.
MEMORIES ARE THE BEST
KIND OF TREASURE AND THIS
BOOK IS YOUR ALADDIN'S
CAVE TO DIP INTO AND
ENJOY FOR YEARS TO COME.

Writing and drawing implements:

pencils,

pens,

charcoal,

crayons,

inky thumbs.

Sticking implements:

glue,

tape,

stapler with staples,

stickers,

Blu-tack.

But most importantly:

your eyes and ears!

Declutter that coat. What's inside?
Draw it. Yuck!!!

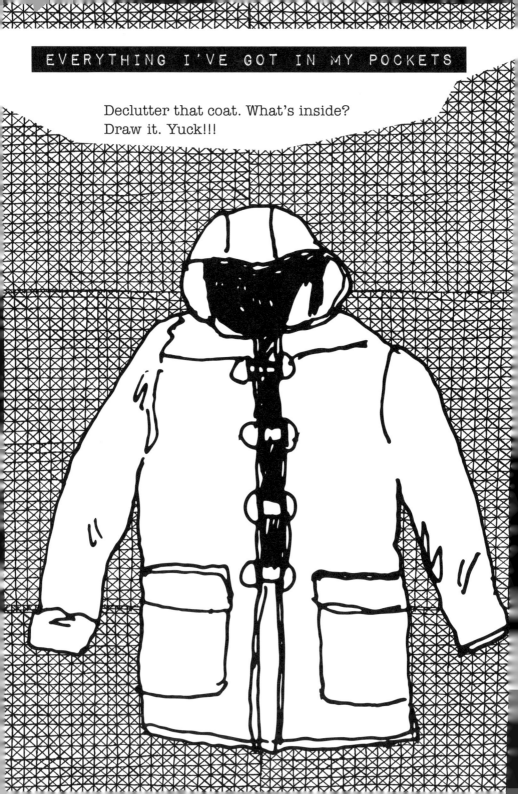

Something small but significant in the general scheme of things. Write it down or draw it.

> Example: *A snail appeared from nowhere on my houseplant. He looked up at me as if to say, 'Yes, you deserve those shoes that you saw in the shop window. Go buy them!' So I did.*

I SPY IN THE PARK

Can you spy the following in the park?

a discarded blob of gum

WHERE......................... WHEN...................

a declaration of love on a park bench

WHERE......................... WHEN...................

someone playing truant

WHERE.......................... WHEN...................

a toddler having a tantrum

WHERE.......................... WHEN...................

someone feeding the birds

WHERE.......................... WHEN...................

So you're never short of the verbal equivalent of a death blow!
Write them here.

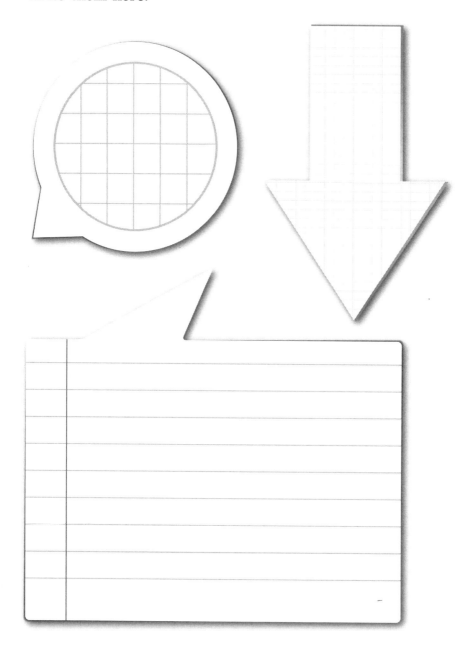

Write a track list of your favourite songs that transport you back to special times. Write what they remind you of.

A

B

SIMPLE JOYS:
GREAT TO DO WHEN YOU'RE FEELING BLUE

Things that are good. Count your blessings here.

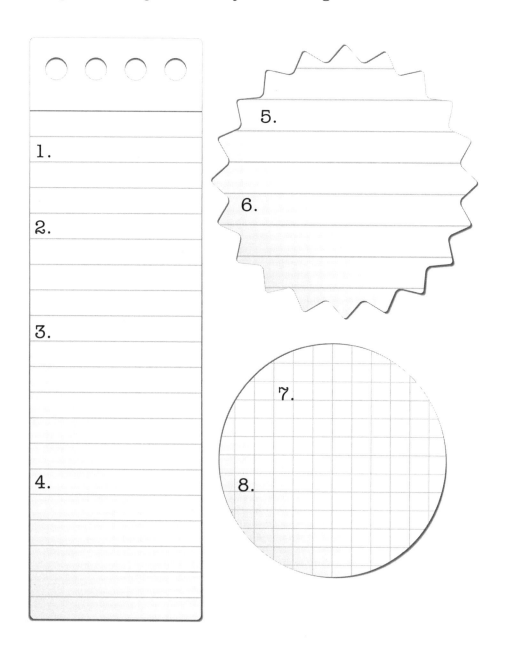

1.

2.

3.

4.

5.

6.

7.

8.

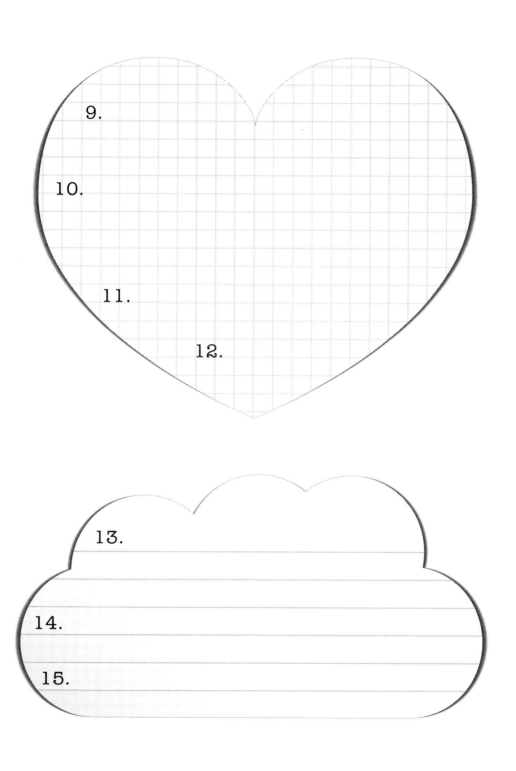

GOAL!

When you've done something really great, write about it and when you achieved it, tear out the page, scrunch it up and 'SCORE!' it in the bin.

THE FIRST SPRING DAY

Pick up something to remind you of it and stick it on the page. Helpful pointer: it must be flat; yes, those little bouncy lambs are super-cute but you can't take them home.

Reward yourself for a job well done. Cut out a rosette and write your latest achievement on it for all to see. Wear it with pride.

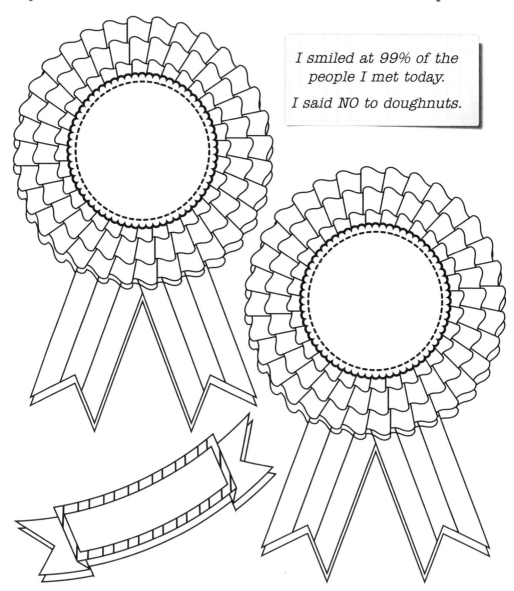

I smiled at 99% of the people I met today.

I said NO to doughnuts.

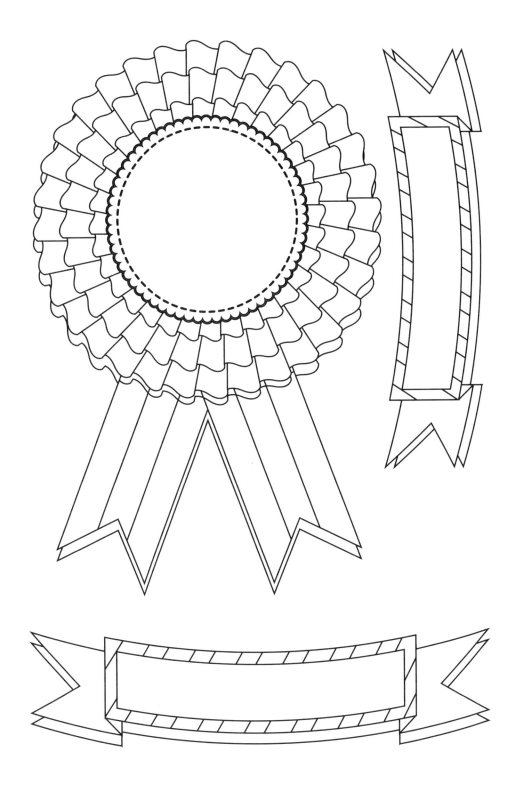

Draw or write it down – preferably as soon as you've had it. Once it's down on paper it won't seem nearly as bad: those big vampire slugs just need a dash of salt and they're toast!

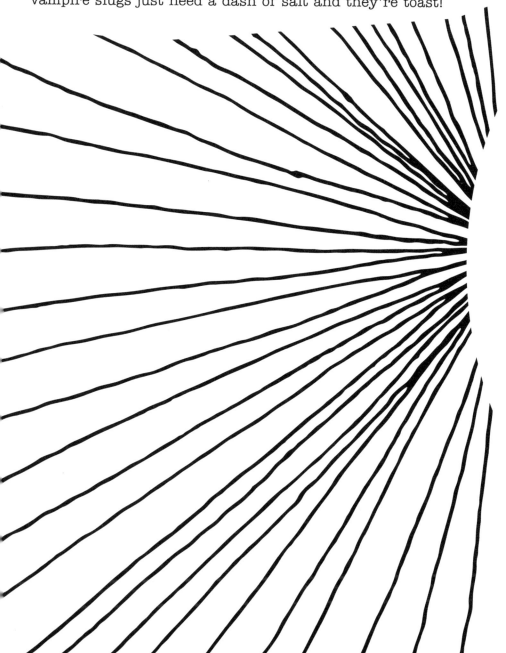

Me.

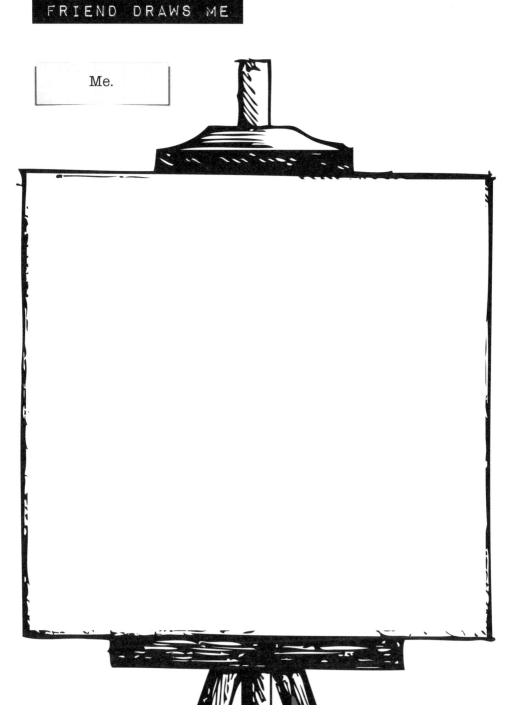

Pick a moment when you're both looking good, i.e. when you look like you've just stepped out of a salon, and preserve this moment in time by asking your friend to capture your best side in a portrait. Draw them too, and don't forget to date it.

My Best Friend.

I LOVE FRINGES

Draw everyone you know, pets included, with a fringe.

Write a poem about your favourite food.

Example: I've never seen a fish with fingers
But I think they're really great,
I think it's because they're crunchy
And brighten up my plate.

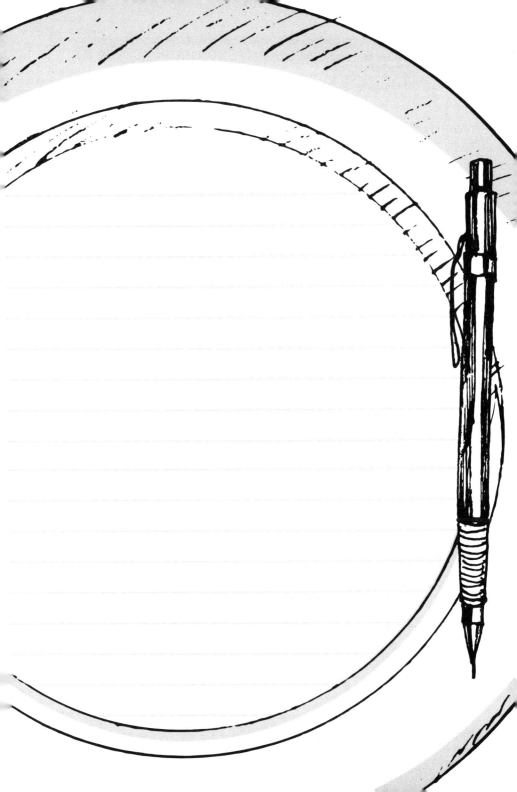

A MEMORABLE CONVERSATION I HAVE HAD WITH...

Write down some of your most memorable conversations here. They could be with your mum, your best friend or a stranger you met on the street, as long as they're not boring.

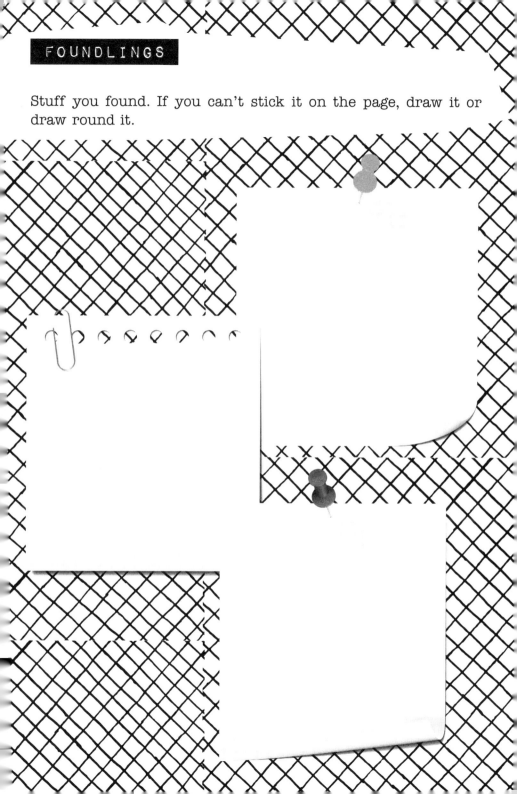

FOUNDLINGS

Stuff you found. If you can't stick it on the page, draw it or draw round it.

Keep the memory alive of a drink you had that was significant – a first date or meeting the in-laws, perhaps – by peeling the label off the bottle. We all do it, don't we?

Get yourself a sugar fix and treat yourself to your favourite sweet after working really hard or doing something scary. Stick the wrapper in the book and write about the BIG thing you achieved that day.

Stick in the ticket to somewhere you visited for the first time.
Describe the journey or place, or doodle a few things that you
want to remember.

When..

Where...

When..

Where...

When...

Where...

When...

Where...

AN OVERHEARD CONVERSATION

This could be something you heard on the bus or the train, or even half a conversation when someone was on their mobile.

We all have a crush on someone famous, so why not indulge it.
Write a dream scenario where you meet your favourite person.

Where will it be?

What will you say to them?

What happens next?

PASSPORT PICTURES

Preserve those cringeworthy pictures and document your hairstyles over the years by sticking in those leftover passport photos from your drawer of memories.

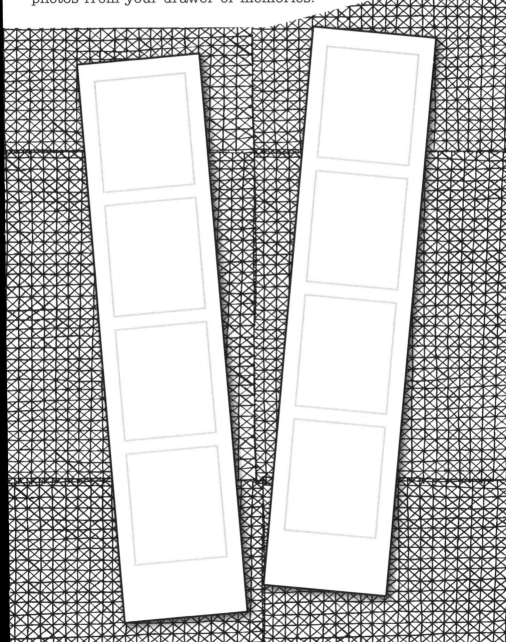

Don't just consign them to the bottom of the drawer – you'll never look at them again – instead pick your favourites and stick them in here.

FROM............................... WHEN...............................

FROM............................ WHEN.................................

LEAVES ARE FALLING FROM THE SKY; IT MUST BE AUTUMN

Pick up leaves – as many different colours as you can find – and press them in these pages. See if you can identify each species.

Draw these maps that are only of use to you.

The map of things I lost behind the sofa

The map to my best treasure in the house

Now tear them out and hide them where prying eyes can't find them.

CLOUD FORMATIONS

Those puffy clouds that look like cats, dogs, trains and two-headed people are cumulus clouds.

Draw some good ones here, or take photographs and stick them in.

Write a track list of your favourite songs for when you're in a romantic mood. The inclusion of a Barry White song, though optional, is strongly encouraged.

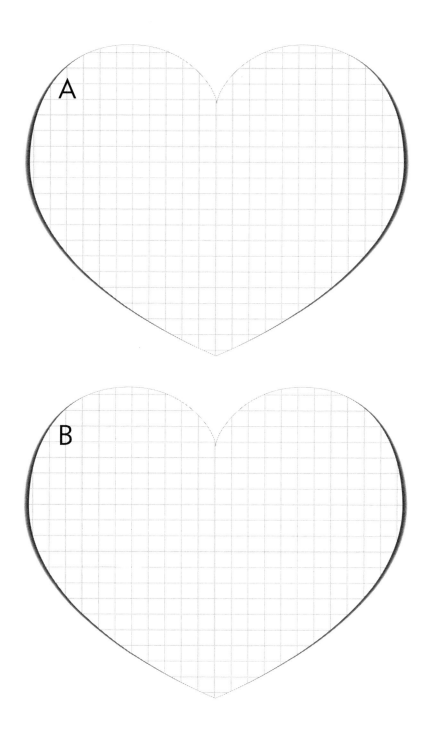

Find six numbers on discarded pieces of newspaper/train tickets/letters and stick them on the page. Now, if you're old enough, buy a lottery ticket with those numbers and stick it on the facing page.

BOUGHT AT..   ON........................

BOUGHT AT..   ON........................

FAVOURITE TWEETS

'Tweet tweet' and then it's gone! Write down your favourite tweets so you can re-read them at your leisure.

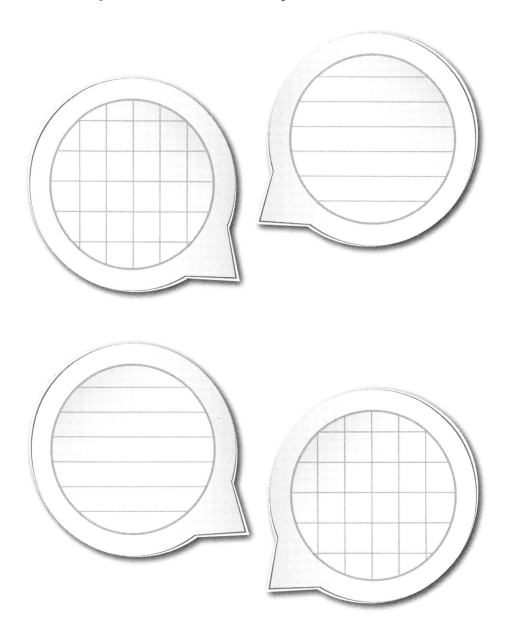

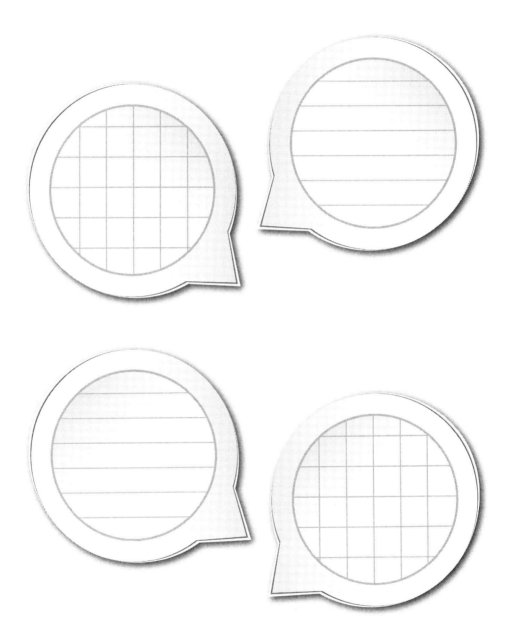

It's bound to happen sooner or later – your exciting, thrill-a-minute life WILL be made into a blockbuster movie. Put the details here:

Leading role:

Love interest:

Comedy sidekick:

Opening title music:

Opening monologue:

Credits music:

Design the movie poster:

Draw your favourite things in the treasure chest.

MY BEST SELFIE

Everyone has a favourite picture of themselves – stick it in here and admire. If you're feeling a bit low, just whip out this beaut and say, 'You're smokin'!' If you can't find a photo, draw yourself looking your very best.

FAVOURITE HAUNTS

Say you were a ghost – where would you haunt? A favourite place or maybe a person who deserves a fright? Get these important decisions down now, just in case. Add some pictures to make it truly chilling.

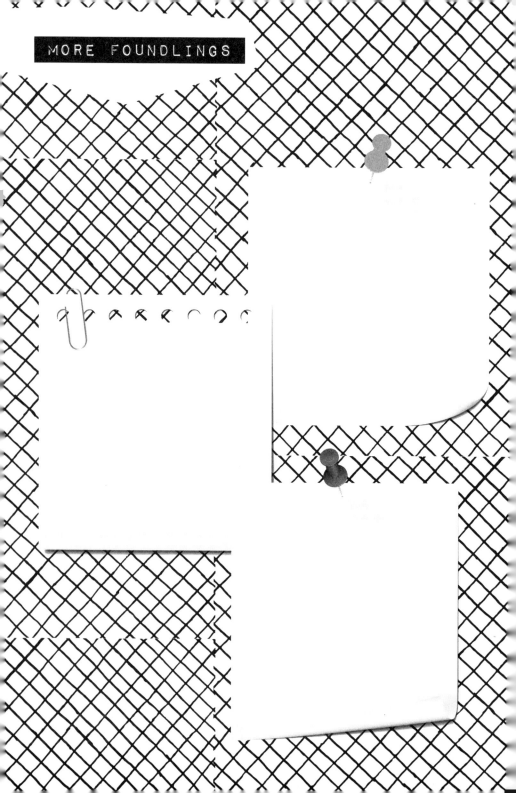

Mmm, a new flavour tea or some particularly lovely packaging
– stick it in.

MY FAVOURITE BOOKS

Print out the cover of a much-loved book and write a review.

Once a week, mark on the barometer how good you feel and date it.

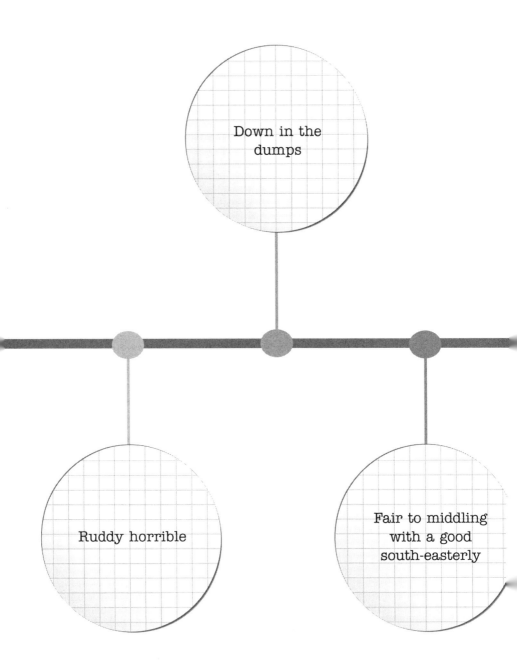

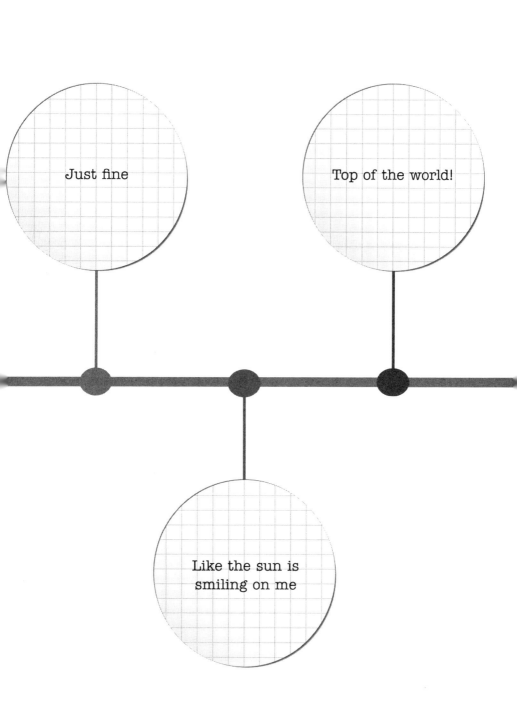

DISTANT SHORES

Keep those holiday memories alive. Pick up postcards and bits of tat from foreign travels and stick them in here. Create the mood – the colours, new words that you learned, leaflets of places you visited, a receipt, a travel ticket, the phone number of that special person who made your heart beat a little faster...

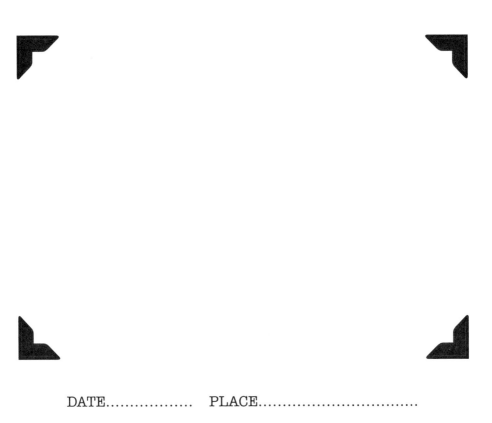

DATE................ PLACE..............................

DATE.................. PLACE...................................

DATE.................. PLACE...................................

Almost as exciting as the holiday itself – travelling on a plane, a boat or a coach – those prison-standard trays with 'unusual' food combos, the noisy sleep buddy, the turbulence, the chatty pilot/driver, the worrying about DVT – bank those memories here.

I SPY IN THE SUPERMARKET

Can you spy the following in the supermarket?

a squashed grape on the floor

WHERE......................... WHEN...................

a broken egg

WHERE......................... WHEN...................

a child on a scooter

WHERE.......................... WHEN.................

a fish with its eyes still in

WHERE.......................... WHEN.................

milk made from nuts

WHERE.......................... WHEN.................

MARMITE STUFF

OK, this is a nicer way of saying 'I HATE IT' or 'I LOVE IT!'

Write those Top Tens and date them – see if they still ring true in the next month or two.

	HATE IT	DO I STILL FEEL THIS WAY?
1.		
2.		
3.		
4.		
5.		
6.		
7.		
8.		
9.		
10.		

LOVE IT	DO I STILL FEEL THIS WAY?
1.	
2.	
3.	
4.	
5.	
6.	
7.	
8.	
9.	
10.	

Draw a picture of someone you really admire, or simply write their name – could be a writer, a pop star, the guy that runs the sweet shop down the road – and write a fan letter to them on the facing page.

Do your 'real' friends sometimes let you down? Well it's time to build your perfect friend. Fill in the list of character traits:

Coolness rating	/10
Geekiness rating	/10
Hair colour	
Best personality trait	
Best physical attribute	
Socks or no socks?	

Now draw a picture of them and keep it in mind the next time you are hoping to find a new friend.

I SPY IN THE CAFE

Can you spot these things in the cafe?

a couple meeting illicitly

WHERE......................... WHEN...................

someone bunking off school

WHERE......................... WHEN...................

a small dog hoovering up crumbs

WHERE.......................... WHEN.................

a meringue

WHERE.......................... WHEN.................

a birthday cake

WHERE.......................... WHEN.................

Mourn your hair's passing and stick a lock of it in here. Give it a little smiley face – see, that's better.

Write and draw your best and worst haircut memories here.

FINGER PAINTING

Regress to a time when holding a pencil was just too much like hard work and express yourself with some paint on your fingers.

Things to paint:
favourite person, self-portrait,
pet, favourite view, etc.

IT WAS THE BEST OF TIMES, IT WAS THE WORST OF TIMES

List your best and worst moments this year.

List the best and worst moments in your life.

SOMEONE ELSE'S URGENT POST-ITS OR SHOPPING LISTS

It's great to find other people's lists, isn't it?
Stick a few in here.

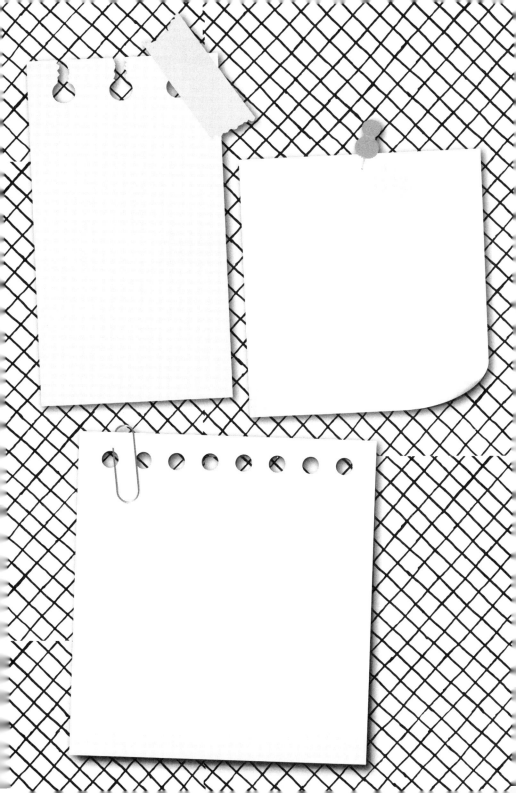

ABSTRACT EXPRESSIONISM:
THE BASICS

Draw a good mood, date it and write why you were feeling like the cherry on the cake.

Draw a bad mood, date it and write why you were feeling like a seagull just expelled yesterday's lunch all over your head.

Wear a beret if it helps.

COULD I HAVE YOUR AUTOGRAPH?

You know how it is: you're minding your own business at the National Gallery, admiring the Botticelli, when you look over to your left and David Bowie is standing there. What do you do? Well, you whip out your copy of *Memory Stick* and turn to this page and ask very sweetly if he'll sign his name for you, that's what.

Draw/stick in a photograph of all the houses you have lived in and write your favourite memory from each place. You could draw a floor plan to make sure you remember all the quirky hiding places you used to use as a child.

CREATE A MEMORY

Who says only the exciting things get to be remembered? Create a memory of today, no matter how humdrum it has been, by writing down every little thing you've seen, heard, thought or said today. Or, if you are the king or queen of the mundane and haven't left your bed all day, just draw the view from where you are.

THE BEST DAY EVER

Now that you've recorded your life at its most pedestrian, it's time for your most exciting, exhilarating, sensational day! It can be a day that really happened or a made-up day that combines all the best things you've ever done, seen and been a part of.

SUMMER'S HERE

Stick in a couple of your favourite summer photos, add some sand and a dash of seawater and you're there. Write down the sights, sounds and smells.

WHERE............................. WHEN.....................................

MY FAVOURITE THING...

MY FAVOURITE SMELL...

MY FAVOURITE PLACE...

WHERE............................. WHEN.....................................

MY FAVOURITE THING...

MY FAVOURITE SMELL..

MY FAVOURITE PLACE..

ABSTRACT EXPRESSIONISM: YOUR FAVOURITE PLACE

Think about your favourite place in the world – it could be your own room, the place you go to hang out with your friends or maybe even Disneyland. Write it down on the note page and draw the feeling on the easel.

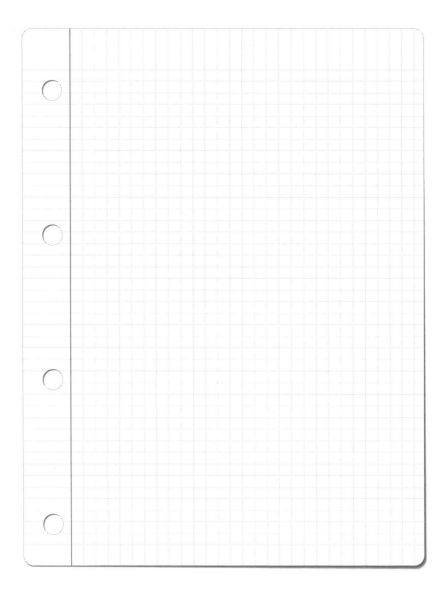

List favourite words you find in the dictionary, along with their definition, by playing the dictionary game, e.g. page 297, right-hand column, tenth word down: dudee/dudhee: short clay pipe.

publication	page number	column	number on page

word	definition	date	when I used it

MY BEST DREAM

Draw or write it down — preferably as soon as you've had it.
Write down every detail and draw what you saw.

WALKING IN A WINTER WONDERLAND

The mercury has dropped and you find yourself wearing socks to bed – it must be winter!
List your favourite things about this season.

I SPY AT THE FAMILY GET-TOGETHER

Can you spy the following?

a drunk aunty

WHERE........................ WHEN...................

dad-dancing

WHERE........................ WHEN...................

someone raiding the fridge

WHERE........................... WHEN..................

wine rings on the coffee table

WHERE........................... WHEN..................

crisps squashed into the sofa

WHERE........................... WHEN..................

A MEMORABLE CONVERSATION I HAVE HAD WITH...

Conversations can be memorable for lots of different reasons – they could be side-splittingly funny, painfully heartfelt or just plain peculiar. Write down some of your most memorable conversations on this page.

Write a track list of your favourite songs that act as pick-me-ups when you're feeling down.

A

B

GOAL!

When you've done something really great, write about it and when you achieved it, tear out the page, scrunch it up and 'SCORE!' it in the bin.

Things that are good. Count your blessings here.

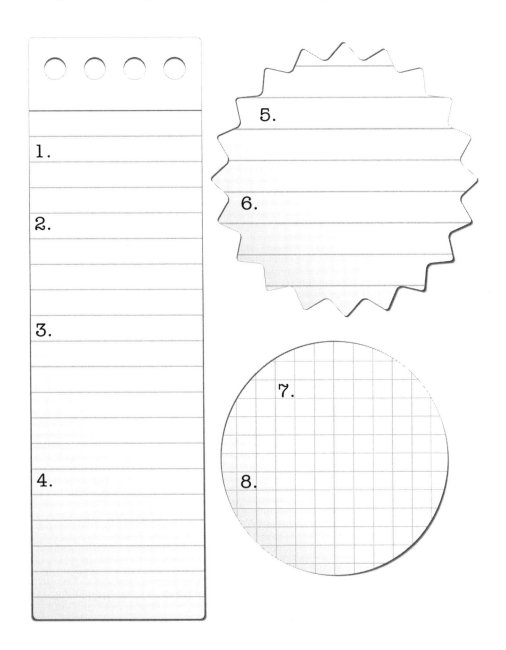

1.

2.

3.

4.

5.

6.

7.

8.

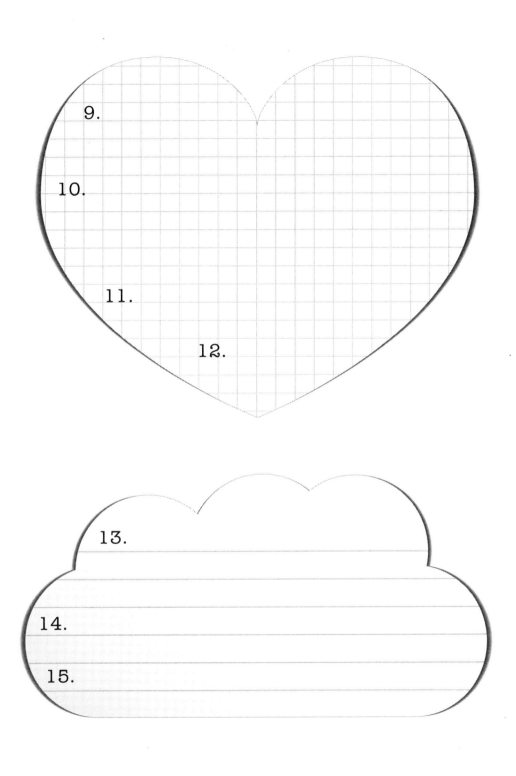

9.

10.

11.

12.

13.

14.

15.

Cinema tickets – stick them in, date them and write a review of the film.

FILM...
WHEN...
WHAT I THOUGHT OF IT........................
....
....

FILM...

WHEN..

WHAT I THOUGHT OF IT...................
....
....

FILM...

WHEN..

WHAT I THOUGHT OF IT...................
....
....

IN THE EVENT OF A ZOMBIE APOCALYPSE...

Use this page to plan what you'd do in the event of the dead rising from the grave. How would you stay alive? Would you barricade yourself into a pub, a shopping mall, or hit the road? Would you arm yourself with a chainsaw or a cricket bat? Your life depends on it!

If you find yourself with nothing do to in a busy public place, e.g. your friend is running late to meet you in the park or you're waiting for a bus, take a look around you and make up back stories for the strangers you see.

Sadly, all pets grow up and eventually go to the big pet shop in the sky – but that doesn't mean we don't remember them fondly. Draw your dearly departed pets here with halos and angel wings, and write their names and what they were like.

After the runaway success of your biographical film, a big-budget Broadway adaptation is inevitable. You should probably plan it now:

Type of musical (e.g. light-hearted comedy à la Gilbert & Sullivan, rock opera, etc.):

A snippet of lyrics from one of the songs:

Song titles

The opening number:

The end of act extravaganza:

The big finish:

Design the show poster:

Keep track of your globetrotting by colouring in every country you've been to on this map. Choose a colour for each type of holiday below and colour the countries accordingly.

[ ] Family Holiday

[ ] Romantic Getaway

[ ] Far-flung Adventure

[ ] Partying with Friends

Get your family, friends and assorted loved ones (pets included) to dip their palms in paint and place a handprint on this page. If you're just too popular to fit everyone in, why not just make thumb prints?

Reward yourself for a job well done. Cut out a rosette and write your latest achievement on it for all to see. Wear it with pride.

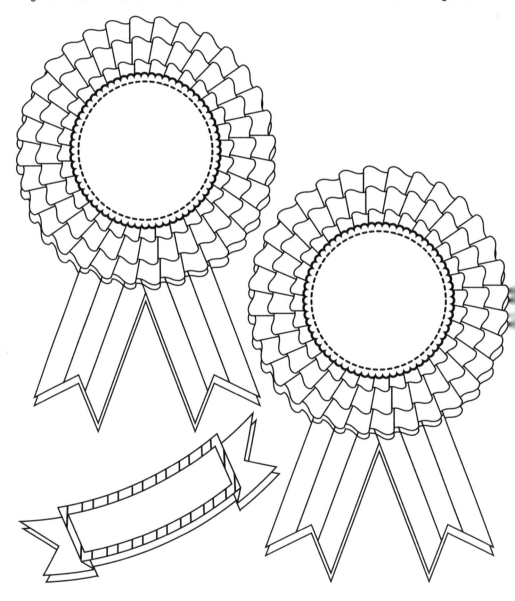

Examples: I decluttered my room.

I asked .... out.

I helped an old lady with her shopping.

I made dinner for my parents/housemates/self.

I did some exercise.

CLOTHES HAVE MEMORIES

Some clothes hold memories; not just specks of ketchup when you were at your friend's barbecue. Perhaps you have a special top that has come to signify a special meeting or life-changing moment but, horror of horrors, you've grown out of it or worse still you snagged it on something and you're not great at darning, so what do you do? Cut a good-sized square of it out and stick it in your book, that's what.

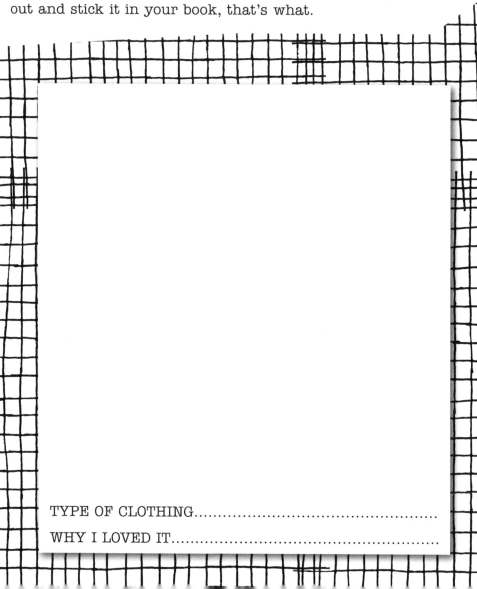

TYPE OF CLOTHING..

WHY I LOVED IT..

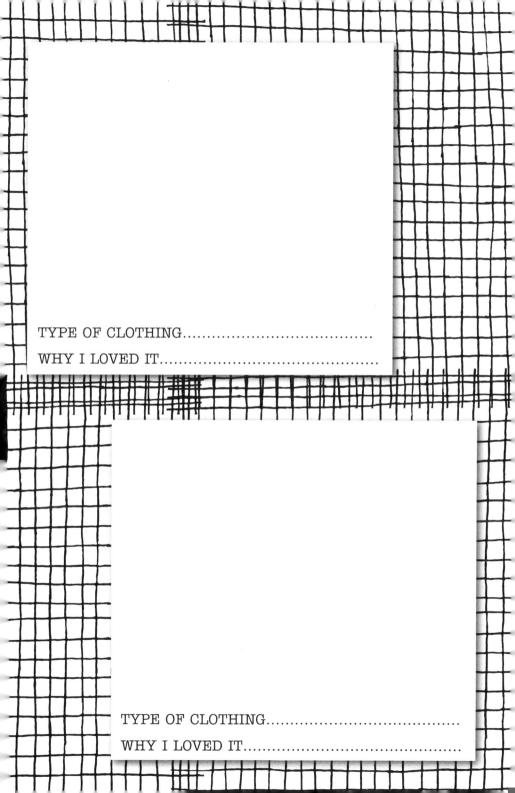

TYPE OF CLOTHING....................................

WHY I LOVED IT..

TYPE OF CLOTHING....................................

WHY I LOVED IT..

MY FAVOURITE WEBSITES I FOUND BY ACCIDENT

It's going to be a long list, so here are a couple of pages.

http://
....

http://
....

http://
....

http://
....

http://
....

http://
....

http://
....

http://
....

http://
....

http://
....

http://
....

http://

....

http://

....

http://

....

http://

....

http://

....

http://

....

http://

....

http://

....

http://

....

http://

....

ABSTRACT EXPRESSIONISM:
DOING SOMETHING SCARY AND NEW

Try to remember the scariest, most daring thing you've done. It could be starting at a new school or job, bungee-jumping, holding a tarantula or striking up a conversation with a certain someone. Write down how it made you feel and go wild with colours and shapes to illustrate that feeling.

You've reached the end! It's time for you to have the last word. Choose your favourite word, write it HUGE across this page and decorate it with how it makes you feel and what it makes you think of.

If you're interested in finding out more about our products, find us on Facebook at **HuckAndPucker** follow us on Twitter at **@HuckandPucker**.

www.huckandpucker.com